Tom and Ricky

and the

Motorcycle Race Mystery

Bob Wright

High Noon Books
Novato, California

Cover Design: Nancy Peach
Illustrations: Herb Heidinger

Glossary: practice, tomorrow, yesterday, lose, early, tank

International Standard Book Number: 0-87879-366-6

10 09 08 07 06 05 04 03
15 14 13 12 11 10

You'll enjoy all the High Noon Books.
Write for a free full list of titles.

Contents

CHAPTER 1

Practice at the Track

It was hot that day. Tom and Ricky were sitting in front of Ricky's house. They didn't have anything to do.

"What do you want to do?" Ricky asked.

"I don't know. There isn't anything to do. It's too hot," Tom answered.

"I have an idea," Ricky said.

"What is it?" Tom asked.

"Let's go out to the track," Ricky said.

"The track? Why?" Tom asked.

"The motorcycle riders are going to practice for the races tomorrow," Ricky said.

"Do you think we can get in to see them?" Tom asked.

"I don't know. They don't let anyone in to see them practice. But let's try," Ricky said.

"OK. Come on," Tom said.

"I want to see Red Miller. He's the best. I want him to win tomorrow," Ricky said.

"I hope he wins both races," Tom said.

They got on their bikes. They went down Front Street. Then they went by the creek. Then they saw the trees next to the track.

"Let's put our bikes here in the trees," Ricky said.

"Why?" Tom asked.

"So no one will see them," Ricky answered.

They hid their bikes. Then they walked over to the fence.

"Look at them practice going around the track," Tom said.

Then they went over to the gate. Sergeant Collins, their friend, was there.

"Hello, boys. Did you come to see the practice today?" he asked.

"We sure did. We want to see Red Miller," Ricky said.

"There he is," Sergeant Collins said.

They all looked in at the track. Red Miller had a red hat, a red coat, and a red motorcycle.

"Now you know why they call him Red," the Sergeant said.

"I wish we could get closer," Tom said.

"You can. Go on in. You can get in free today," Sergeant Collins said.

Tom and Ricky went in at the gate. They found a good place to sit.

There were a lot of racers out on the track.

"Look at him go," Ricky said.

The red motorcycle raced around the track. A green motorcycle was out there, too.

"Who's that?" Tom asked.

"That's Rocky Slag. He's fast, too. But he's not as fast as Red Miller," Ricky said.

"He's almost as fast," Tom said.

"I don't like Rocky Slag," Ricky said.

"Why not? What don't you like about him?"
Tom asked.

"He's almost as fast," Tom said.

"He will do anything to win. He's been trying for a long time to beat Red Miller," Ricky said.

"I hope Red wins tomorrow," Tom said.

"He will. He's a good racer. He has a good motorcycle. He knows what he is doing," Ricky said.

Tom and Ricky saw Red Miller race and race around the track.

Then Ricky said, "It's getting late. It's time to go home."

"I wish we could stay a little longer," Tom said.

"I wish we could, too. But we can't," Ricky said.

They walked out the front gate. Sergeant Collins was still there. "Will you be out here tomorrow?" he asked.

"You bet we will," Ricky said.

"Where are your bikes?" the Sergeant asked.

"We hid them. They are in the trees next to the fence," Tom said.

"That was a good idea. I'll be here tomorrow. I'll see you then," Sergeant Collins said.

Tom and Ricky got their bikes. Then they both went home.

"I'll be at your place early tomorrow," Tom called out.

CHAPTER 2

The Gas Can

Ricky woke up early on Saturday. The sun was already out. He had to get ready to meet Tom.

His mother called out, "What's up? What's the rush? It's Saturday."

"I know that. I have to meet Tom," he said.

"What are you going to do?" she asked.

"We're going to the motorcycle races," Ricky answered.

Just then Ricky's dad came in. "So you're going to the motorcycle races," he said.

"Right. We want to get there early. We want to get good seats," Ricky said.

"Is Red Miller going to be there?" his dad asked.

"He sure is. That's why we're going. Do you want to go with us?" Ricky asked his dad.

"I'd sure like to. I have to stay here and work on the car," his dad said.

"The car? What's wrong with it?" Ricky asked.

"I don't know. It's going too slow. I have to find out what's wrong," he said.

"How long has that been going on?" Ricky asked.

"For about a week," his dad answered.

All of a sudden Patches began to bark.

"Patches, what is it?" Ricky asked.

Patches kept on barking. Then he ran to the front door.

"I bet that Tom is here," Ricky said.

Ricky ran to the front door. Tom was there. "Are you ready?" Tom asked.

"I sure am. Let's get going," Ricky said.

Patches ran out of the house. "No, Patches. You stay here," Ricky said.

Patches looked at Tom and Ricky. Then he went back into the house.

Ricky got on his bike. They went the same way as before. But this time there were lots of people going to the track.

"Let's put our bikes in the same place," Ricky called out.

"That's a good idea. They'll be safe there," Tom answered.

They got off their bikes and hid them. Tom looked over the fence. "Look, there's Red Miller."

Red was sitting on his motorcycle. His men were with him. Red was getting ready.

"Good luck," Ricky yelled.

Tom yelled, too.

Red Miller saw Tom and Ricky. He waved to them. Then he started his motorcycle.

Ricky called to Tom, "Come on. The race is going to start."

"Wait. Look at this," Tom said.

"What?" Ricky answered.

"This can by the fence," Tom said.

"It looks like a gas can," Ricky said.

"It is a gas can. But what is it doing here by the fence?" Tom asked.

"I don't know. But I don't think it's safe. Is there any gas in it?" Ricky asked.

"There sure is," Tom said.

"Put it down. Someone must know it's there. Come on. We have to get into the track," Ricky said.

Tom and Ricky ran up to the gate.

"I have the money," Ricky said. He gave the man the money. Then they went running in.

"Hurry up. The motorcycles are on the track," Ricky called to Tom.

There were a lot of people at the track.

"It is a gas can. But what is it doing here by the fence?"

Tom and Ricky got good seats. They could see everything.

"There they go," Tom yelled.

All the people yelled.

The race was on.

CHAPTER 3

Red Miller Gets Mad

The race was on. The motorcycles raced around the track. All the people were yelling.

"Can you see Red Miller?" Ricky yelled.

"No. Where is he?" Tom yelled. He was looking all over the track.

"Wait a minute. There he is," Ricky said.

"I don't see him. Where is he?" Tom asked.

"There. See him?" Ricky said.

"I see him. He is not winning. Who is in front of him?" asked Tom

"Rocky Slag is in front. Red will pass him. Wait and see," Ricky yelled.

The motorcycles raced around the track. Everyone was yelling. There was a lot of dust. It was hard to see.

Tom yelled, "Is Red winning now? Do you see him?"

"I see him. He is not winning. Rocky is still winning," answered Ricky.

Red Miller was not going very fast. His motorcycle was too slow.

Tom saw Red come by.

"He is going too slow. His motorcycle went faster yesterday," he said.

Ricky saw Red, too.

"He is too slow. Other motorcycles are ahead now," Ricky said.

"What is wrong? Why is he so slow today?" Tom asked.

"I don't know. He has to go faster. He will not win," Ricky answered.

The motorcycles went around and around. Red Miller went slower and slower.

Then the race was over.

Tom yelled, "Oh, no. Red came in last!"

Ricky yelled, "Rocky Slag won the race!"

Tom and Ricky sat down. They didn't feel too good.

"Why did Red go so slow today?" asked Ricky.

"He was faster yesterday. Why was he faster yesterday? What's going on?" Tom asked.

The people got up. It was time to go home.

Tom and Ricky got up, too. They went out the gate.

"Come on. Let's get the bikes," Ricky said.

"OK. Let's go home," Tom said.

They went to the bikes. Tom went to the fence. He looked over.

"Ricky. There's Red Miller," he called.

Red Miller sat on his motorcycle. His men were with him. He looked mad.

Tom and Ricky could hear him. "Why did this motorcycle go so slow today? What is wrong with it?"

The men did not know. They looked at the motorcycle.

"We don't know why it was slow. It looks OK," they said.

"It is *not* OK. It's too slow!" Red Miller yelled.

Red Miller got off the motorcycle. He walked away. He was mad.

Tom looked down.

"Ricky. The gas can is still here," he said.

"It is?" Ricky said.

"Yes. Here it is," Tom said.

"I think we should tell Red's men about it," Ricky said.

Tom looked at the men.

"I don't think so. The men look mad, too. I don't want to talk to them now," he said.

Ricky said, "They do look mad. Come on. Let's go home."

They got the bikes out from the trees.

"Maybe Red will win tomorrow," Tom said.

"I hope so," Ricky said.

"He better go faster. He could lose tomorrow, too," Tom said.

Tom and Ricky rode their bikes back to Ricky's house.

Ricky got off his bike. "See you in the morning," he said.

"OK," Tom said.

CHAPTER 4

Ricky Has an Idea

Ricky put his bike away. He went in the house. He was mad that Red didn't win.

"How did the race go?" his mother asked.

"Rocky Slag won the race. Red Miller came in last," Ricky said.

"That's too bad. I know you wanted Red Miller to win," she said.

"Red can still win tomorrow. Where is Dad?" Ricky asked.

"He is still fixing the car," she said.

Ricky went outside. Patches ran up to him. Patches barked and wagged his tail.

"Hello, Patches. Come on. Help me find Dad," said Ricky.

Patches barked again. He ran to the front of the house. Ricky's father was in the car.

"Hi, Dad," Ricky called.

"Hi, Ricky. Want to come for a ride?" his father called.

Ricky got in the car. Patches got in, too.

"Did you fix the car?" Ricky asked.

"I think so. I want to try it out. I want to see if I fixed it," his dad answered.

Ricky's father took the car over to Front Street.

"Is it OK now?" Ricky asked.

"Yes. I think it is OK now," his father answered.

"There was some water in the gas tank. That's why the car was so slow."

"What was wrong?" Ricky asked.

"There was some water in the gas tank. That's why the car was so slow," his father answered.

"How did you get it fixed?" Ricky asked.

"I had to take out all the gas. I had to clean everything. Then I had to put in new gas," his dad said.

"How did water get in the gas tank?" Ricky asked.

"I don't know. It is OK now. We can go home," his father said.

They went back home in the car. Patches jumped out of the car. Then he started to bark.

"What's up, Patches?" Ricky asked.

"He is barking at the gas can. I had to get that gas can for the old gas in the car," Ricky's father said.

Ricky had an idea. He ran into the house. He went to the phone.

Ricky called Tom on the phone.

"Hi, Tom. This is Ricky," he said.

"Hi, Ricky," Tom said.

Ricky said, "I have an idea. I think I know why Red Miller lost the race today."

"How could you know that?" Tom said.

"I think it was his gas. I think there was water in his gas," Ricky said.

"Water in his gas? How could there be water in his gas?" Tom asked.

"You saw the gas can. It was by the fence. Someone must have put it there. Someone must have put water in Red's gas," Ricky said.

"You could be right. What can we do?" Tom asked.

"We can go to the track. We can go early. That way we can see who takes the can," Ricky said.

"OK. Good idea," Tom said.

"Come by early tomorrow," Ricky said.

"OK. I'll see you then," Tom said.

Ricky looked at his dad.

"What's up, Ricky? You seem to be thinking about something," his dad said

"I sure am," Ricky said.

"What is it?" his dad asked.

"I think that Red Miller is going to win that race tomorrow," Ricky said.

CHAPTER 5

The Man and the Gas Can

The next morning Ricky was waiting for Tom. He was on his bike in front of his house. The sun wasn't even up yet it was so early. Ricky saw Tom coming down the street.

"Tom, here I am," Ricky called out.

"Why are we going to the track so early?" Tom asked.

"Come on. Let's get going. I'll tell you on the way," Ricky said.

They started down to the track.

"OK. Fill me in," Tom said.

"The first day we went to the track we didn't see a gas can, did we?" Ricky asked.

"No. We saw it yesterday," Tom said.

"That's right. That's the day Red didn't win," Ricky said.

"So what's the can have to do with it?" Tom asked.

"My dad had to fix his car yesterday. There was water in the gas. That made the car go slow. My dad had to clean everything. He put new gas in the car. Then it worked fine," Ricky said.

Tom just looked at Ricky. He wasn't sure what was going on. Ricky was trying to tell him something. But what?

"Do you think someone didn't want Red to win? Do you think someone put water in Red's gas?" Tom asked.

"I sure do," Ricky answered.

"Maybe that can does have something to do with all of this," Tom said.

They got to the track. They hid their bikes in the trees. Then they sat by their bikes.

"No one can see us here," Ricky said.

"Can you see the can? Is it still there by the fence?" Tom asked.

"Yes, it's still there," Ricky answered.

"We can just sit and wait," Tom said.

Then they saw someone coming over to the fence.

"Look. See that man. He's inside the track," Ricky said.

"He's walking over this way," Tom said.

The man did not walk fast. He stopped and looked around. Then he kept on walking to the fence.

"Do you think he can see us?" Tom asked.

"No. Not here in the trees," Ricky answered.

The man stopped by the fence. He looked at the gas can. He picked it up. He looked around. Then he took the can over to Red Miller's motorcycle.

The man opened the gas can. Then he put the gas in Red's motorcycle.

Tom said, "Ricky. You were right."

The man was done. He took the gas can back to the fence. He put the gas can by the fence. Then he walked away.

He looked around. Then he took the can over to Red Miller's motorcycle.

"Did you see that?" Tom asked.

"I sure did," Ricky answered.

"What can we do?" Tom asked.

"We can tell Sergeant Collins. Come on," Ricky said.

"Yes. Sergeant Collins can help us," Tom said.

"He can tell Red Miller," Ricky said.

"I hope Sergeant Collins is here," Tom said.

"Me, too. Come on," Ricky said.

Tom and Ricky ran to the gate. They ran to find Sergeant Collins.

CHAPTER 6

Sergeant Collins Helps Out

Tom and Ricky got to the gate. They looked for Sergeant Collins. There were a lot of people waiting to get in.

"Where is he? I don't see him," Ricky said.

"There he is," Tom said.

They yelled to Sergeant Collins. Then they ran over to him.

"Hello, Tom. Hello, Ricky. Is anything wrong?" Sergeant Collins said.

Tom said, "Yes. Something is wrong."

"What is it?" Sergeant Collins asked.

Ricky said, "We got here early. We came to see the gas can. A man put gas in Red Miller's motorcycle."

Sergeant Collins looked at Ricky. "What gas can? What are you talking about?" he asked.

Tom said, "There is a gas can by the fence. We think there is water in that can. A man put some in the motorcycle."

Sergeant Collins said, "Are you sure about that? Come with me. Let's find Red Miller."

They went back to the gate. Sergeant Collins let them in. They all walked around the race track.

Sergeant Collins found Red Miller.

"These boys want to talk to you. They have something to tell you," he said.

Tom said, "We think we know why you didn't win yesterday. A man put water in your gas. We saw him."

Ricky said, "There is a gas can by the fence. It's over there. A man came and put some in your motorcycle."

Red Miller said, "I don't see a gas can. Are you sure?"

"Come with us," Ricky said.

They all went over to the fence.

"Look. There it is," Tom said.

Red Miller got the can. He opened it. He looked in the can.

"There is water in here. There is some gas.

But there is a lot of water," he said. Red just kept

looking at the can.

"There is water in here. There is some gas. But there
is a lot of water."

Sergeant Collins asked, "How did you see the man?"

Ricky said, "We got here early. We sat under the trees."

Red Miller said, "Where is the man?"

"There he is right there. That's the man," Tom yelled.

Red Miller said, "It can't be. He is one of my men. He works for me."

Sergeant Collins called to the man.

The man walked over to them.

Red Miller was mad. "Did you put water in the gas?" he asked.

Sergeant Collins said, "These boys saw you with the gas can. There is water in the gas can."

The man looked at Tom and Ricky. He looked at Sergeant Collins. Then he looked at Red Miller. He could see that Red was mad.

The man said, "Yes. I did it. Rocky Slag gave me money to do it."

"Let me at him," Red said.

"No. I'll take care of him," Sergeant Collins said. He took the man away.

Red Miller looked at Tom and Ricky. "Thank you. Now I know why I was slow. Now I can win," he said.

Red Miller called to his men, "Put new gas in the motorcycle and clean it up. We don't have a lot of time. Get going!"

Red Miller looked at Tom and Ricky.

He said, "You can stay here. You can see the race with my men. It's a good place."

Red Miller got on his motorcycle. The race would start soon.

CHAPTER 7

The Big Race

It was time for the race. Red Miller was ready to win. Tom and Ricky sat with Red's men.

"Red will win the big race today," Ricky said.

"He sure will," one of Red's men said.

The motorcycles raced and raced around the track. Red was ahead of everyone. And he stayed ahead. Rocky tried to pass him. But he couldn't. Red's motorcycle seemed to get faster and faster. No one could keep up with Red.

Then the race was over. Everyone yelled. Everyone wanted Red to win. And he did. One of the men looked at Tom and Ricky. "You made Red win," he said.

Red came over in his motorcycle. "You made me win. Now, come on with me. I want to see Rocky."

Rocky was mad. He thought he would win.

Red was mad, too. "I know what you did, Rocky. You gave money to one of my men. He put water in my motorcycle."

"What is this all about?" Rocky asked.

"The man told us everything. And these boys saw him do it. You better not try it again. You're getting off lucky this time," Red said.

Red walked away. Then he called to Tom and Ricky. "Would you like to sit on my motorcycle?" he asked.

"Do we ever!" Ricky said.

Tom and Ricky both got on the motorcycle. Red told his men, "It's OK. They're my friends."

"We have to go now," Ricky said.

"Look. I race a lot in this town. From now on, you get in free. And you can always sit here with me and my men. OK?" he asked.

"You bet," Ricky said.

They went back to their bikes.

"What a day it's been," Tom said.

"It sure has," Ricky answered.